Literacy BASICS

FOR AGES 6-7 KEY STAGE 1

Contents

Look and learn

Some **letter patterns** are very common. They are very helpful for spelling.

a b**ee** in a tr**ee**   a b**ea**st on the b**ea**ch   a t**oa**d on the r**oa**d   a cr**ow** in the sn**ow**

Practice

Make some words.

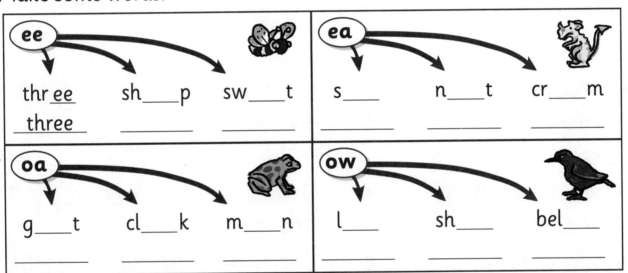

ee

thr <u>ee</u>   sh___p   sw___t
<u>three</u>   _____   _____

ea

s___   n___t   cr___m
_____   _____   _____

oa

g___t   cl___k   m___n
_____   _____   _____

ow

l___   sh___   bel___
_____   _____   _____

Challenge

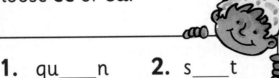

Choose **ee** or **ea**.

1. qu___n   2. s___t
3. m___n   4. w___p
5. s___d   6. cl___n
7. gr___dy   8. p___ch
9. m___l   10. asl___p

Choose **oa** or **ow**.

1. c___t   2. gr___
3. thr___   4. t___st
5. s___k   6. wind___
7. g___t   8. yell___
9. sl___   10. l___d

Word order

Look and learn

We have to write words in the **correct order** so they **make sense**.

bark. Dogs can ☒

Dogs can bark. ☑

Practice

Write these sentences correctly. Remember the capital letters and full stops.

1. Fish swim water. in <u>Fish swim in water.</u>
2. hop. to like Kangaroos _____
3. read I well. can _____
4. sky The is blue. _____
5. to It began rain. _____
6. eating horse My apples. likes _____
7. roaring was The loudly. lion _____
8. Monkeys trees. climb can _____

Challenge

Tick ☑ the sentences that make sense. Cross ☒ those that are not sensible.

1. The bone bit the dog. ☐
2. The tree climbed a squirrel. ☐
3. The boy ate a sandwich. ☐
4. The workman drank a cup of tea. ☐
5. The tune whistled a girl. ☐
6. The flowers planted the gardener. ☐
7. The pencil wrote with the boy. ☐
8. The man fell off the wall. ☐
9. The television was watching the children. ☐
10. The mouse chased the cat. ☐

Adding ed and ing

Look and learn

We can add **ing** and **ed** to the end of many words.

Yesterday I play**ed** in the park.

Today I am play**ing** in the bedroom.

Practice

Complete this chart.

	verb	+ ing	+ ed
1.	kick	kicking	kicked
2.	walk		
3.	pull		
4.	jump		
5.	mix		
6.	knock		
7.	splash		
8.	wash		
9.	lift		
10.	plant		

Challenge

Add **ed** to the end of these verbs. Take care with the spelling!

Set A

hop   hopped

pat   _____

hum   _____

tip   _____

beg   _____

Set B

bake   baked

dive   _____

score   _____

use   _____

race   _____

Set C

hurry   hurried

marry   _____

carry   _____

empty   _____

copy   _____

Vowels and consonants

Look and learn

There are 26 **letters** in the alphabet. There are 5 **vowels**: **a,e,i,o** and **u**. All the other letters are **consonants**.

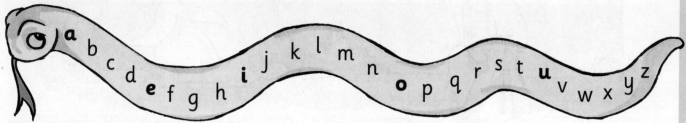

Every word usually has **at least one** vowel in it.

Practice

Underline the vowel in each word.

1. hats	**2.** net	**3.** mop
4. bell	**5.** zip	**6.** rug
7. fog	**8.** hut	**9.** tap
10. hen	**11.** tin	**12.** sock
13. cup	**14.** sack	**15.** wig

Challenge

Think of a suitable vowel to complete each word.

1. j__g	**2.** r__d	**3.** v__t	**4.** r__b
5. v__n	**6.** b__y	**7.** g__rl	**8.** w__y
9. b__rk	**10.** b__rn	**11.** c__rl	**12.** d__wn

Now write the words you made in the correct sets.

words with **a**	words with **e**	words with **i**	words with **o**	words with **u**

Making sense of sentences

Look and learn

Sentences should **make sense** when you read them.

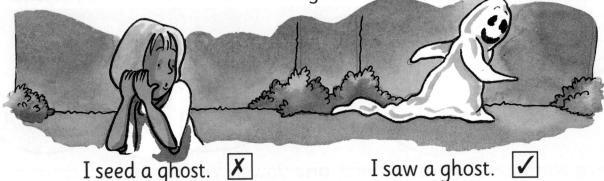

I seed a ghost. ☒   I saw a ghost. ☑

Practice

Choose the correct word to complete each sentence.

1. Sam __caught__ the ball.   (catched / caught)
2. The children _____ running.   (was / were)
3. I fell over and _____ myself.   (hurt / hurted)
4. Emma _____ to school by bike.   (goed / went)
5. Joel has _____ his leg.   (broked / broken)
6. Ann _____ home as soon as possible.   (came / camed)
7. The boy _____ crying.   (was / were)
8. I _____ it yesterday.   (done / did)
9. He _____ speak clearly.   (don't / doesn't)
10. I _____ only just got up.   (has / have)

Challenge

There is a word in each sentence that is not needed. Cross it out.

1. The squirrel climbed up ~~and~~ the tree.
2. I broke Tom's his pencil.
3. I couldn't not find my book.
4. The lady saw where Ben he was.
5. The teacher got into in her car.
6. The girl returned it the ruler.
7. Tom and Anna were ran on ahead.
8. Edward climbed got out of bed.

Look and learn

A **conjunction** is a **joining** word. It may be used to join **two sentences** together.

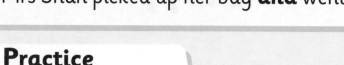

Mrs Shah picked up her bag. She went to the shop.
Mrs Shah picked up her bag **and** went to the shop.

Practice

Make each pair of sentences into one sentence. Use the word **and**.

1. I went to the market. I bought some apples.
    _____

2. I got undressed. I went to bed.
    _____

3. Sam boiled the kettle. She made a cup of tea.
    _____

4. Zak sat down. He watched the television.
    _____

5. Sita opened her desk. She took out her book.
    _____

6. Mr Brand went into the garden. He cut the grass.
    _____

Challenge

Finish off each sentence in your own words.

1. Katie likes skating but _____
2. The monkey climbed the tree and _____
3. Shireen hurt herself when _____
4. I kept playing until _____
5. I had a wash because _____
6. It began to rain so _____

Look and learn

Being able to **rhyme** can help you with your **spelling**.

Jack and **Jill**
- went up the **hill**.
- had a **pill**.
- felt quite **ill**.
- went to the **mill**.

Practice

Choose a word from the box to rhyme with each word below.

rain	stay	bite	bone	moon
high	flew	look	pull	good

1. spoon ___moon___

2. kite _____

3. today _____

4. grew _____

5. stone _____

6. pain _____

7. sigh _____

8. wood _____

9. bull _____

10. book _____

Challenge

Match up the pairs of rhyming words. They sound alike but have different letter patterns.

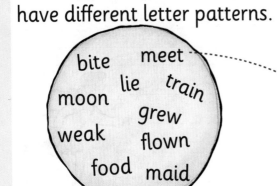

bite   meet
moon   lie   train
grew
weak   flown
food   maid

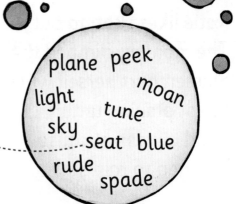

plane   peek
light   moan
tune
sky   seat   blue
rude
spade

Look and learn

In spelling we have to learn how to **build up** words.

cl + ow + n = clown

Practice

Build up these words.

1. sh + ou + t = _____
2. l + ou + d = _____
3. m + ou + th = _____
4. r + ou + nd = _____
5. cl + ou + d = _____
6. c + ou + nt = _____
7. c + ow = _____
8. cr + ow + n = _____
9. ow + l = _____
10. fl + ow + er = _____
11. v + ow + el = _____
12. t + ow + el = _____

Challenge

Underline all the **ou** and **ow** words in these sentences.

1. Ali saw a <u>mouse</u> in his <u>house</u>.
2. Just now I saw a brown cow.
3. Does an owl growl?
4. Please don't shout about it!
5. I found a pound on the ground.
6. There was a flower on my towel.
7. The proud man spoke in a loud voice.
8. Go south at the mouth of the river.
9. There are five vowels in the alphabet.
10. The queen wears a crown on her head.

Look and learn

My name is Amir.

What is your name?

A **sentence** often finishes with a **full stop**.

A **question** always finishes with a **question mark**.

Practice

Put in the missing full stops and question marks.

1. When is your birthday
2. It is in March
3. How old are you
4. I am seven
5. Where do you live
6. I live in Newcastle
7. What do you like best at school
8. My favourite subject is art

Challenge

Rewrite these sentences correctly.

1. how many children are there in your class

   _____

2. some children like to keep pets

   _____

3. do you have any brothers or sisters

   _____

4. what is the weather like today

   _____

5. who is your favourite singer

   _____

6. tom and emma are good friends

   _____

Look and learn

Sometimes it is helpful to put words in **groups**.

tools
saw
hammer
pliers

drill

bed

furniture
table
chair
settee

Practice

Sort out these words into groups.

bee	guitar	France	ladybird
drums	Italy	ant	Spain
piano	Germany	recorder	beetle

insects	countries	musical instruments
bee		

Challenge

Circle the odd word out in each group.

1.	lion bear (cup) tiger	**2.**	jacket pencil shirt jumper
3.	book bus car lorry	**4.**	cup saucer bowl ruler
5.	apple potato carrot onion	**6.**	cat dog mouse table
7.	cottage light house bungalow	**8.**	desk apple orange banana
9.	kitchen bedroom lounge garden	**10.**	aunt uncle mother sister
11.	pigeon robin sparrow hedgehog	**12.**	horse baker dentist teacher

Look and learn

Antonyms are words that are **opposite** in meaning.

happy   unhappy

Practice

Choose the words that mean the opposite.

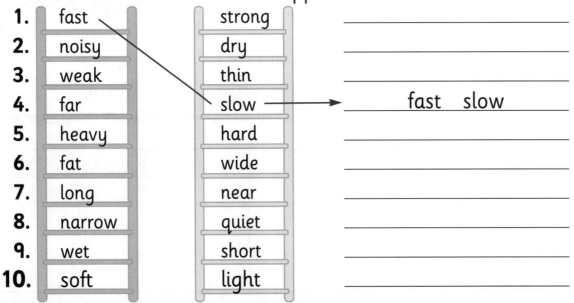

1.	fast	strong	_____
2.	noisy	dry	_____
3.	weak	thin	_____
4.	far	slow →	fast slow
5.	heavy	hard	_____
6.	fat	wide	_____
7.	long	near	_____
8.	narrow	quiet	_____
9.	wet	short	_____
10.	soft	light	_____

Challenge

Choose the prefix **un** or **dis** to make each word mean the opposite.

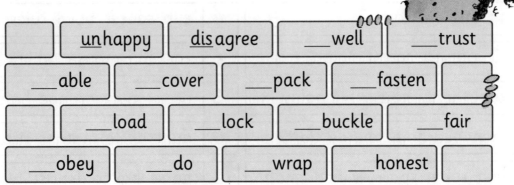

<u>un</u>happy	<u>dis</u>agree	___well	___trust
___able	___cover	___pack	___fasten
___load	___lock	___buckle	___fair
___obey	___do	___wrap	___honest

Compound words

Look and learn

Compound words are made up of **two smaller words** joined together.

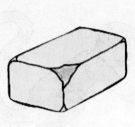

butter   +   fly   =   butterfly

Practice

Do the word sums to make the compound words.

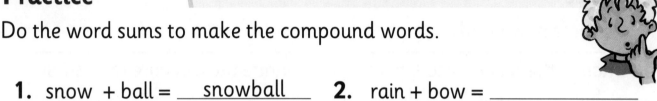

1. snow + ball = __snowball__

2. rain + bow = _____

3. sun + shine = _____

4. moon + light = _____

5. foot + step = _____

6. hand + bag = _____

7. play + time = _____

8. arm + chair = _____

9. tooth + brush = _____

10. sand + castle = _____

Challenge

Match up pairs of words to make some more compound words.

1. hedge	ball	_____
2. foot	mark	_____
3. home	hog	__hedgehog__
4. book	hole	_____
5. back	work	_____
6. key	way	_____
7. table	bone	_____
8. water	about	_____
9. run	fall	_____
10. round	cloth	_____

Look and learn

We can often make new words by **changing some letters**.

book

look   **c**ook   **h**ook

We can often find **smaller words** hiding **inside larger** words.

sh**ape**

Practice

Make some new words.

1. Change the **h** in **h**air to f, p, ch ___fair___ ___pair___ ___chair___	**2.** Change the **c** in **c**are to d, sc, st _____ _____ _____
3. Change the **w** in **w**ear to b, t, p _____ _____ _____	**4.** Change the **p** in **p**ort to f, s, sh _____ _____ _____
5. Change the **s** in **s**aw to j, cl, str _____ _____ _____	**6.** Change the **m** in **m**ore to w, sn, sc _____ _____ _____

Challenge

Find the name of an animal or insect hiding in each word.

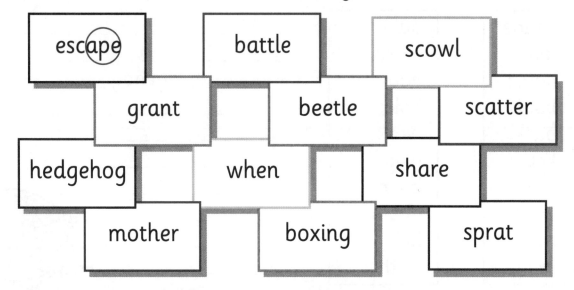

escape   battle   scowl

grant   beetle   scatter

hedgehog   when   share

mother   boxing   sprat

Speech marks

Look and learn

Speech marks show us someone is speaking. We write everything the person says **inside** the speech marks.

I live in a cave.

I live in a castle.

The dragon said, "**I live in a cave**."   "**I live in a castle**," the knight replied.

Practice

Write the words from the speech bubbles **inside** the speech marks.

I live in a web.

I live in a burrow.

I live in the sea.

I live in a pond.

1. The spider said, "_____."

2. "_____," the rabbit replied.

3. The fish said, "_____."

4. "_____," the frog replied.

Challenge

Write something you think each person might say.

1. The builder said, " <u>I build houses</u> ."
2. The teacher said, "_____."
3. The doctor said, "_____."
4. The plumber said, "_____."
5. The farmer said, "_____."
6. The vet said, "_____."
7. The hairdresser said, "_____."
8. The author said, "_____."

Look and learn

Two common letter patterns are **wh** and **ph**.

wheel

ele**ph**ant

Practice

Find the five **wh** and five **ph** words in the puzzle.

a	b	c	d	e	f	g	h	w	h	y	j
q	w	h	e	e	l	p	o	n	m	l	k
r	s	t	e	l	e	p	h	a	n	t	y
a	l	p	h	a	b	e	t	y	x	w	v
z	a	b	c	d	e	w	h	a	l	e	f
g	h	p	h	o	t	o	g	r	a	p	h
d	o	l	p	h	i	n	j	k	l	m	o
y	x	u	t	s	r	q	p	w	h	e	n
z	w	h	e	r	e	a	b	c	d	f	g
h	i	k	l	m	p	h	a	n	t	o	m

wh words

when	where
why	wheel
	whale

ph words

dolphin	elephant
alphabet	phantom
	photograph

Challenge

Choose **wh** or **ph** to complete each word.

1. _wh_ at	**2.** or____an	**3.** ____en	**4.** ____o
5. gra____	**6.** ____ere	**7.** ne____ew	**8.** ____y
9. ____onics	**10.** ____antom	**11.** ____ich	**12.** ____istle
13. ____isker	**14.** ____ite	**15.** al____abet	**16.** ____rase

Syllables

Look and learn

When you say long words slowly you can hear that they can be **broken down** into **smaller chunks** called **syllables**.

com – pu – ter

(three syllables)

Tap out the syllables when you count them.

Practice

Make these two-syllable words.

1. yel + low = _____yellow_____   2. sis + ter = _____

3. un + cle = _____   4. al + ways = _____

5. Fri + day = _____   6. be + cause = _____

7. sud + den = _____   8. an + gry = _____

9. joy + ful = _____   10. ba + by = _____

11. good + ness = _____   12. quick + ly = _____

Challenge

Say these words slowly. Write if each word has two or three syllables.

1. dinosaur (_3_)   2. carpet (_2_)   3. garden (___)

4. churches (___)   5. tomato (___)   6. cabbage (___)

7. somebody (___)   8. anyone (___)   9. aeroplane (___)

10. picture (___)   11. skating (___)   12. motorway (___)

13. tonight (___)   14. careful (___)   15. remember (___)

Verbs

Look and learn

Verbs tell us what someone or something is **doing**.

A kangaroo **hops**.

Practice

Choose the best verb to complete each sentence.

fly	swim	squeaks	roar	slides
chatters	hops	bark	purrs	crawl

1. Fish ___swim___ .

2. A frog _____ .

3. A snail _____ .

4. Birds _____ .

5. Beetles _____ .

6. A mouse _____ .

7. A cat _____ .

8. Lions _____ .

9. Dogs _____ .

10. A monkey _____ .

Challenge

Choose the correct form of the verb to fill each gap.

1. The wind _____ to blow. (beginned / began)

2. I _____ a lovely picture. (drew / drawed)

3. Tom _____ down the stairs. (fell / falled)

4. The birds _____ into the tree. (flied / flew)

5. My uncle _____ me a present. (gived / gave)

6. The man _____ the bell. (rang / ringed)

7. Emma _____ in the sea. (swimmed / swam)

8. I _____ my best clothes. (wore / weared)

9. The lady _____ a letter. (writed / wrote)

10. The dog _____ the cat. (saw / seed)

Look and learn

Always check to make sure your **sentences make sense**.

Tom has forgotten to finish his sentence.

Emma has rubbed out the beginning of her sentence.

Yesterday I ...

... came to tea.

Practice

Match up the beginning and ending of each sentence.

1. You cut paper   an ice cream.
2. The girl ate   out of the pond.
3. In the rain we   with scissors.
4. We had a picnic   spinning a web.
5. I drew a line   need an umbrella.
6. The frog jumped   with a ruler.
7. I saw a spider   ticked loudly.
8. The clock   in the park.

Challenge

Think of a good way to begin each sentence. (Remember to begin with a capital letter!)

1. _____ with a hammer.
2. _____ in the night.
3. _____ after lunch.
4. _____ an old car.
5. _____ in the garden.
6. _____ through the tunnel.
7. _____ the sea.
8. _____ crashed into the wall.

Look and learn

The letter patterns **er**, **ir** and **ur** make a similar sound.

k**er**b   sh**ir**t   n**ur**se

Practice

Write the words in the chart.

herd	churn	bird
turn	stir	dirt
jerk	term	curl
girl	herb	church
verse	purse	first
curve	skirt	stern
firm	person	burn
serve	fur	third

er	ir	ur
herd	bird	churn

Challenge

Match up the pairs of words that rhyme.

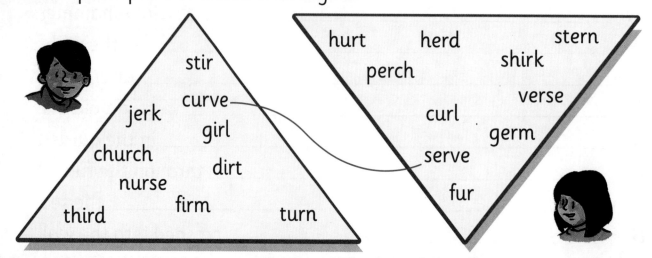

stir
jerk
curve
church
girl
nurse
dirt
third
firm
turn

hurt
perch
herd
curl
serve
fur
stern
shirk
verse
germ

Look and learn

Always check your writing to see if you have made any silly mistakes.

The children **was** reading. X   The children **were** reading. ✓

Practice

Tick ✓ the sentences that are correct. Cross X the sentences that are wrong.

1. I does my writing neatly. ☐
2. The dogs was barking loudly. ☐
3. A man is digging his garden. ☐
4. The lady went shopping. ☐
5. It are very cold today. ☐
6. They always come on a Thursday. ☐
7. Tom try hard with his spelling. ☐
8. My cat like milk. ☐
9. Frogs hops. ☐
10. The sports car goes very fast. ☐

Challenge

Think of a suitable word to complete each sentence.

1. The ships _____ sailing on the sea.
2. Mrs Brown _____ shopping in the market.
3. Victoria _____ the ball to Amy.
4. The box was very _____ .
5. Lots of _____ were flying in the sky.
6. My _____ are painting and collecting shells.
7. _____ was eating his dinner.
8. The _____ hooted twice.
9. The cars _____ going far too fast.
10. My friend and I _____ looking for Josh.

Look and learn

In spelling you have to **look** very carefully.

| a | b | c | n | e | a | r | g |

| c | l | e | a | r | m | n | p |

| h | f | e | a | r | j | k | l |

Practice

Find the 10 **ea** words in the puzzle.

hear

a	b	d	h	e	a	r	f	g	h
z	d	e	a	r	k	l	m	n	o
p	q	r	s	t	u	f	e	a	r
v	w	x	y	n	e	a	r	z	a
b	g	e	a	r	g	h	i	j	k
l	m	n	o	p	q	y	e	a	r
c	l	e	a	r	t	u	v	s	w
x	y	z	y	r	e	a	r	c	d
e	f	g	h	i	j	t	e	a	r
k	a	p	p	e	a	r	q	m	n

Challenge

Divide these **ea** words into sets.

head	heat	dead
leap	ready	speak
bear	teach	wear
spread	steam	easy
eagle	thread	steady

ea sounds like **e** in b**e**d	**ea** sounds like **e** in m**ee**t
head	heat

Commas

Look and learn

Commas are used to **separate** things in a **list**.

Penguins, monkeys, elephants, camels, lions, tigers ...

Practice

Fill in the missing commas in these lists.

1. mice rats gerbils hamsters and guinea pigs
2. potatoes onions carrots cabbages and sprouts
3. apples pears oranges bananas and grapes
4. cups saucers plates bowls and dishes
5. curry pizza sausages pasta and fish
6. cars lorries bikes buses and vans
7. red orange yellow green and blue
8. guitar piano trumpet trombone and flute

Challenge

Write a list of what each person needs.

bandages	shampoo	ladder	helmet	hose	flippers
boots	axe	spade	goggles	shorts	comb
medicines	brush	rake	snorkel	shirt	thermometer
fork	stethoscope	ball	wet suit	mower	mirror

1. A hairdresser needs <u>shampoo, a comb, a brush and a mirror</u> .
2. A firefighter needs _____ .
3. A footballer needs _____ .
4. A gardener needs _____ .
5. A diver needs _____ .
6. A doctor needs _____ .

Look and learn

Sometimes we can change words by **adding letters** to the **end** of them.

Emma likes to **help**. She is very help**ful**.

(Notice the spelling of **ful** at the end of the word.)

Practice

Do the word sums and make some **ful** words.

1. pain + ful = _____ .

2. use + ful = _____ .

3. hope + ful = _____ .

4. care + ful = _____ .

5. power + ful = _____ .

6. thank + ful = _____ .

7. colour + ful = _____ .

8. thought + ful = _____ .

9. help + ful = _____ .

10. truth + ful = _____ .

11. wonder + ful = _____ .

12. faith + ful = _____ .

Challenge

Choose **ful** or **ly** to complete each word.

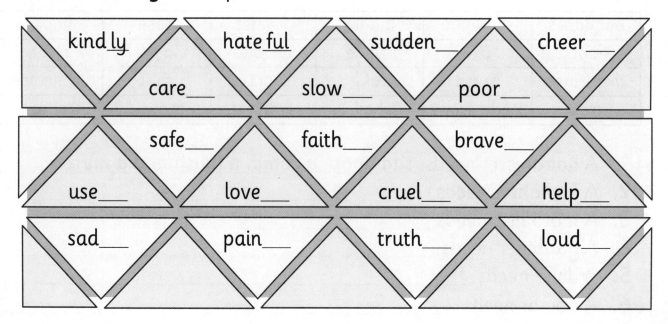

kind <u>ly</u>   hate <u>ful</u>   sudden___   cheer___

care___   slow___   poor___

safe___   faith___   brave___

use___   love___   cruel___   help___

sad___   pain___   truth___   loud___

Look and learn

Whenever you write a **question** you should write a **capital letter** at the beginning and a **question mark** at the end.

What is the time?

Why are you crying?

Where am I?

Practice

Match up each question to the correct answer.

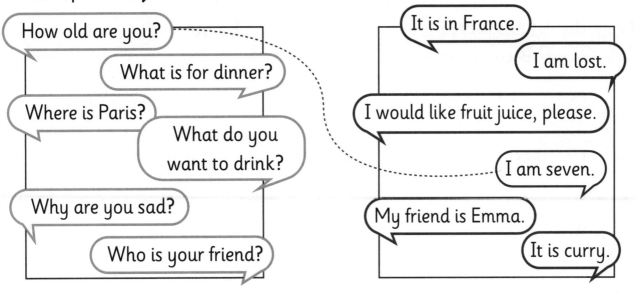

How old are you?

What is for dinner?

Where is Paris?

What do you want to drink?

Why are you sad?

Who is your friend?

It is in France.

I am lost.

I would like fruit juice, please.

I am seven.

My friend is Emma.

It is curry.

Challenge

Here are some answers. Write what you think the questions were.

	Questions	Answers
1.		It is yellow.
2.		I like reading best.
3.		I have a dog.
4.		It is April.
5.		I live in Hull.
6.		I like playing tennis.
7.		It is sunny.
8.		It is seven o'clock.

Exclamation marks

Look and learn

We use an **exclamation mark** when we **feel strongly** about something.

I hate school!

What a lovely present!

Stop shouting!

Practice

Rewrite each sentence correctly and end it with an exclamation mark.

1. this tastes lovely
This tastes lovely!

2. be quiet
_____

3. how nice to see you
_____

4. you must be joking
_____

5. I really love sweets
_____

6. stop thief
_____

7. help
_____

8. it's not fair
_____

Challenge

Choose a question mark or an exclamation mark to end each sentence.

1. Thank goodness you're here _!_

2. How are you __

3. Get out of my way __

4. We had a lovely time __

5. This is awful __

6. Where are you going __

7. Who was in the car __

8. Shut the door at once __

9. Do you like swimming __

10. Look out __

Look and learn

a rabbit

lots of rabbits

Singular means **one** thing.

Plural means **more** than one thing.

Practice

Complete each of these.

1. one shoe, two ___shoes___	**2.** one book, two _____
3. one coat, two _____	**4.** one shirt, two _____
5. one jumper, two _____	**6.** one hat, two _____
7. one_____, two cups	**8.** one _____, two saucers
9. one _____, two pans	**10.** one _____, two plates
11. one _____, two mugs	**12.** one _____, two bowls

Challenge

Rewrite each sentence. Change the underlined words into the plural.

1. The <u>boy</u> picked up the <u>book</u>.
<u>The boys picked up the books.</u>

2. The <u>girl</u> looked at the <u>bike</u>.
_____

3. The <u>dog</u> chased the <u>cat</u>.
_____

4. The <u>builder</u> built the <u>house</u>.
_____

5. The <u>doctor</u> sat on the <u>chair</u>.
_____

6. The <u>monster</u> came out of the <u>cave</u>.
_____

Look and learn

We use **capital letters** at the **beginning** of **sentences**.

My name is **A**bdi.

My name is **S**hireen.

We also use capital letters at the **beginning of special names**.

Practice

Write the names of these people again. Remember the capital letters.

edward Edward	amy	naqish	shanaz
mr gregg	mrs barnes	dr patel	miss shah

Challenge

Complete these lists.

Sunday
_____
Tuesday
_____
Friday
_____

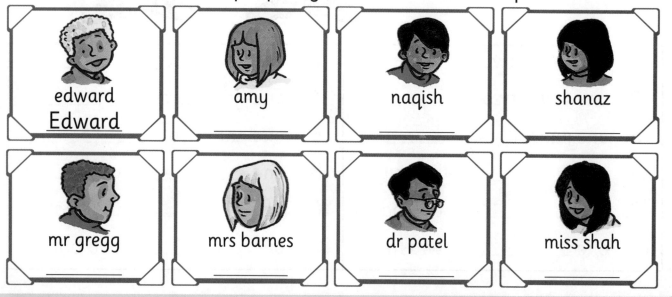

1 January	2 February	3
4	5 May	6 June
7 July	8	9
10	11 November	12

Look and learn

Synonyms are words with **similar meanings**.

I'm happy.

I'm cheerful.

I'm joyful.

Practice

Choose a synonym from the box to go with each word below.

small	strong	ill	sad	scared
wet	start	hard	quick	silly

1. frightened ___scared___
2. sick _____
3. tiny _____
4. difficult _____
5. foolish _____
6. damp _____
7. begin _____
8. powerful _____
9. unhappy _____
10. fast _____

Challenge

Circle the synonym in each set that goes with the word on the left.

1. closed

empty	big	(shut)

2. tall

high	rough	loud

3. talk

run	mix	speak

4. hop

swim	jump	act

5. rough

sweet	uneven	deep

6. quiet

dark	smooth	silent

7. slim

slender	huge	cold

8. ask

write	request	read

closed

Look and learn

We can **group** some words together because they are **related**.
These are all names of **sports**.

cricket   tennis   golf   rugby

Practice

Sort these words into the correct groups.

arm	coat	apple
orange	neck	hat
head	banana	gloves
grapes	foot	pear
socks	trousers	leg
hand	melon	skirt

parts of the body	fruit	clothes

Challenge

Name four different types of:

1. tree	sycamore,	
2. vehicle		
3. flower		
4. farm animal		
5. vegetable		
6. furniture		
7. drink		
8. musical instrument		

Look and learn

Punctuation marks make writing **easier** to read.

Where are you going?

Tom said where are you going ☒
Tom said, "Where are you going?" ☑

Practice

Fill in the missing punctuation marks in these sentences.

missing
full stop
question mark
exclamation mark
speech marks
commas
full stop
question mark
speech marks

1. The children went to school
2. Have you seen my pencil
3. My house is on fire
4. James said, I will clean the brushes.
5. My favourite colours are red brown yellow and orange.
6. Some cats are black
7. Do you have a pet
8. This bag is heavy, the lady said.

Challenge

Rewrite these sentences correctly.

1. what a lovely surprise

   _____

2. please leave the box on the table

   _____

3. I have been to France Italy Spain and Greece

   _____

4. how many brothers and sisters do you have

   _____

5. I am going shopping said mr hills

   _____

Answers

Page 2
Practice: three, sheep, sweet; sea, neat, cream; goat, cloak, moan; low, show, below
Challenge: 1. queen, 2. seat, 3. mean, 4. weep, 5. seed, 6. clean, 7. greedy, 8. peach, 9. meal, 10. asleep
1. coat, 2. grow, 3. throw, 4. toast, 5. soak, 6. window, 7. goat, 8. yellow, 9. slow, 10. load

Page 3
Practice:
2. Kangaroos like to hop.
3. I can read well.
4. The sky is blue.
5. It began to rain.
6. My horse likes eating apples.
7. The lion was roaring loudly.
8. Monkeys can climb trees.
Challenge: 3., 4., 8. make sense

Page 4
Practice:
ing: kicking, walking, pulling, jumping, mixing, knocking, splashing, washing, lifting, planting
ed: kicked, walked, pulled, jumped, mixed, knocked, splashed, washed, lifted, planted
Challenge:
Set A: hopped, patted, hummed, tipped, begged
Set B: baked, dived, scored, used, raced
Set C: hurried, married, carried, emptied, copied

Page 5
Practice:
2. net, 3. mop, 4. bell, 5. zip, 6. rug, 7. fog, 8. hut, 9. tap, 10. hen, 11. tin, 12. sock, 13. cup, 14. sack, 15. wig
Challenge: 1. jig, jog or jug, 2. rid, red or rod, 3. vet, 4. rib, rob or rub, 5. van, 6. bay, boy or buy, 7. girl, 8. way, 9. bark, 10. barn, born or burn, 11. curl, 12. dawn or down

Page 6
Practice: 2. were, 3. hurt, 4. went, 15. broken, 6. came, 7. was, 8. did, 9. doesn't, 10. have
Challenge: 2. his, 3. not, 4. he, 5. in, 6. it, 7. were, 8. got

Page 7
Practice:
1. I went to the market and bought some apples.
2. I got undressed and went to bed.
3. Sam boiled the kettle and made a cup of tea.
4. Zak sat down and watched the television.
5. Sita opened her desk and took out her book.
6. Mr Brand went into the garden and cut the grass.
Challenge: answers may vary

Page 8
Practice: 2. bite, 3. stay, 4. flew, 5. bone, 6. rain, 7. high, 8. good, 9. pull, 10. look
Challenge: meet/seat, bite/light, moon/tune, weak/peek, food/rude, lie/sky, train/plane, grew/blue, flown/moan, maid/spade

Page 9
Practice: 1. shout, 2. loud, 3. mouth, 4. round, 5. cloud, 6. count, 7. cow, 8. crown, 9. owl, 10. flower, 11. vowel, 12. towel
Challenge: 2. now, brown, cow, 3. owl, growl, 4. shout, about, 5. found, pound, ground, 6. flower, towel, 7. proud, loud, 8. south, mouth, 9. vowels, 10. crown

Page 10
Practice:
1. When is your birthday?
2. It is in March.
3. How old are you?
4. I am seven.
5. Where do you live?
6. I live in Newcastle.
7. What do you like best at school?
8. My favourite subject is art.
Challenge:
1. How many children are there in your class?
2. Some children like to keep pets.
3. Do you have any brothers or sisters?
4. What is the weather like today?
5. Who is your favourite singer?
6. Tom and Emma are good friends.

Page 11
Practice: insects: bee, ant, ladybird, beetle
countries: Italy, Germany, France, Spain
musical instruments: drums, piano, guitar, recorder
Challenge: 2. pencil, 3. book, 4. ruler, 5. apple, 6. table, 7. light, 8. desk, 9. garden, 10. uncle, 11. hedgehog, 12. horse

Page 12
Practice: 2. noisy/quiet, 3. weak/strong, 4. far/near, 5. heavy/light, 6. fat/thin, 7. long/short, 8. narrow/wide, 9. wet/dry, 10. soft/hard
Challenge: unhappy, disagree, unwell, distrust, unable, uncover/discover, unpack, unfasten, unload, unlock, unbuckle, unfair, disobey, undo, unwrap, dishonest

Page 13
Practice: 2. rainbow, 3. sunshine, 4. moonlight, 5. footstep, 6. handbag, 7. playtime, 8. armchair, 9. toothbrush, 10. sandcastle
Challenge: 2. football, 3. homework, 4. bookmark, 5. backbone, 6. keyhole, 7. tablecloth, 8. waterfall, 9. runway, 10. roundabout

Page 14
Practice:
2. dare, scare, stare
3. bear, tear, pear
4. fort, sort, short
5. jaw, claw, straw
6. wore, snore, score
Challenge: ape, bat, owl, ant, bee, cat, hog, hen, hare, moth, ox, rat

Page 15
Practice:
1. The spider said, "I live in a web."
2. "I live in a burrow," the rabbit replied.
3. The fish said, "I live in the sea."
4. "I live in a pond," the frog replied.
Challenge: answers may vary

Page 16
Challenge: 2. orphan, 3. when, 4. who, 5. graph, 6. where, 7. nephew, 8. why, 9. phonics, 10. phantom, 11. which, 12. whistle, 13. whisker, 14. white, 15. alphabet, 16. phrase

Page 17
Practice: 2. sister, 3. uncle, 4. always, 5. Friday, 6. because, 7. sudden, 8. angry, 9. joyful, 10. baby, 11. goodness, 12. quickly
Challenge: 3. (2), 4. (2), 5. (3), 6. (2), 7. (3), 8. (3), 9. (3), 10. (2), 11. (2), 12. (3), 13. (2), 14. (2), 15. (3)

Page 18
Practice:
2. A frog hops.
3. A snail slides.
4. Birds fly.
5. Beetles crawl.
6. A mouse squeaks.
7. A cat purrs.
8. Lions roar.
9. Dogs bark.
10. A monkey chatters.
Challenge: 1. began, 2. drew, 3. fell, 4. flew, 5. gave, 6. rang, 7. swam, 8. wore, 9. wrote, 10. saw

Page 19
Practice:
2. The girl ate an ice cream.
3. In the rain we need an umbrella.
4. We had a picnic in the park.
5. I drew a line with a ruler.
6. The frog jumped out of the pond.
7. I saw a spider spinning a web.
8. The clock ticked loudly.
Challenge: answers may vary